This book belongs to

....

Disney

Storybook Favourites

Sticker
book

READER'S DIGEST YOUNG FAMILIES

While they fought, Tinker Bell slashed the ropes that bound the boys, and they stopped the pirates from jumping overboard and rowing away in their boat. Then Peter knocked Hook's sword overboard, and Hook jumped, too.

Geppetto had stayed up to finish a merry-faced puppet he was carving. Now he held the puppet up. 'Look, Figaro! Look, Cleo!' he said with a chuckle. 'Isn't Pinocchio almost like a real boy?'

Bambi

While the crowd roared with delight, Dumbo did power dives, loops, spins and barrel rolls. He swooped down to pick up peanuts and squirted a trunkful of water on the clowns.

On through Wonderland Alice went, in search of the White Rabbit. She met two jolly fellows, Tweedledum and Tweedledee.

Cinderella

'How delightful!' the stepsisters said to each other. 'We are going to the palace to a ball!'

'And I – ' said Cinderella, ' – I am invited, too!'

Nor had they ever had such an evening of fun. All the forest folk gathered around the cottage windows to watch them play and dance and sing.

'We'll buy a big house in the country,' said Roger. 'We'll have a Dalmatian plantation!'

And so they did exactly that. And Pongo and Perdita and all the spotted puppies lived there happily ever after.

Lady and the Tramp

Away raced the little pig to his brother's house of sticks. No sooner was he inside, when there came a Knock, Knock, Knock at the door! It was the big bad wolf!

The Ugly Duckling

As he swam away with his new family, he ruffled his feathers and held his head up high. Never before had the Ugly Duckling felt so much love in his heart.

When the sailors rescued them, they thought Pluto had jumped in to save the cat. They called him a hero. They fussed over him, and the mates moved his bed to the captain's cabin.

'What'll we do with Pegleg?' Donald asked.

'Just tie him up for now,' said Mickey. 'We can pack him in with the supplies. There's no space suit for him but that should keep him from freezing while we're on the Moon.'

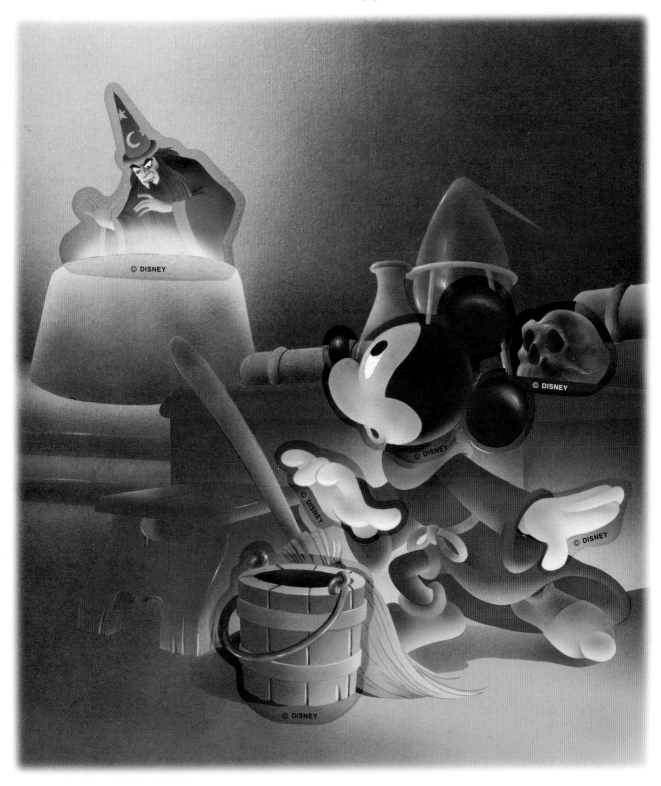

Mickey knew about the magic of the hat.

'If I had that hat,' thought Mickey, 'I would never have to work again.'

Goofy had to dress like a Movie Star. He had whole wardrobes full of clothes.

The naughty chipmunks finished dancing on the branches. Then they hauled all the acorns on board the stolen sailboat.

'Oh, well,' said Donald, watching from his canoe. 'At least I know my boat really will sail.'

All they could see from their window was a
tremendous castle. 'Let's go!' said Mickey. 'Whoever lives in
that big castle must have plenty of food to share!'

Finally they arrived in the city, so tired they could hardly take a step.

'We'll stop and rest at my peaceful pad,' O'Malley said.

At the entrance to the park, Mary Poppins stopped. For there was Bert, a jack-of-all-trades. Bert was down on his knees on the pavement, making pictures in coloured chalk.

Everyone piled back into Mickey's car – with Pluto in the midst of them. And they all went back to Mickey's house to celebrate the triumph with lots of ice cream and cake.

Wart put back the sword into the stone.
Everyone tried, but the sword wouldn't move.
Only Wart could pull it out again. So it was no mistake.

Donald let Chip 'n' Dale drive his fine toy train, while he rode on a coach behind.

'It's much more fun,' said Donald happily, 'to play with folks who are just the right size!'

'Well,' said Mickey, as he cut the cake and handed big slices around. 'It was a good lunch anyway. And we've all learnt a lesson. Donald won't be snatching any more lunch baskets, and we will always invite him to our picnics.'

Aunt Polly was very strict, but she was good to Pollyanna and bought her many lovely new clothes.

Pollyanna danced with happiness. She had never owned any brand-new clothes – only hand-me-downs.

Lucky Puppy

There were Penny and Lenny
and Salter and Pepper
and Jolly and Rolly
and Patch and Latch ...

Out jumped Mickey Mouse waving his sword and shield. Out jumped Minnie and the Mouseketeers. Up jumped all the folks who had been enchanted all over Fantasyland.

Proudly, he led the elephant back to where his father was building the tree house.

'Look, Father, I found an elephant to help us build the tree house!'

No one threw any peanuts to the camels or lions or tigers, which was probably just as well.

'Grumio, you're a genius!' the Toymaker
cheered. He decorated his assistant with ribbons
and badges. 'You shall be Toyland's most
honoured citizen.'

He dug and dug and dug. And what do you think he found?

A big, juicy bone. It was a great big bone for a small dog.

There were lots of presents and a big Christmas tree. But there was a note from Santa, too.

'Dear Donald,' it said, '*whatever you do, remember Santa Claus is watching you!*'

Donald Duck's Christmas Tree

It was a beautiful Christmas tree.

'Now I'll pile the presents under the tree for Mickey and Minnie and for Huey, Dewey and Louie,' said Donald.

© DISNEY

Father Noah had no time to waste. A flood was coming!
God told him to make haste and gather wood, then measure it,
cut it and bind it with pitch.

Birds squawked with excitement and flew through the skies.

'This truck is getting pretty full,' said Ludwig. 'Let's see ...
I found parrots, a zebra, a camel, a polar bear, and now ... all
these monkeys. Let's go to the country and see what we can
find there.'

Disney Storybook Favourites Sticker Book

All illustrations and text copyright © Disney Enterprises, Inc.
Some material based on the Mowgli stories in
The Jungle Book and *The Second Jungle Book* by Rudyard Kipling, and upon
The Hundred and One Dalmations by Dodie Smith, published by William Heinemann Ltd.

Published in 2009 by
The Reader's Digest Association Limited
11 Westferry Circus, Canary Wharf, London E14 4HE

Editor: Rachel Warren Chadd
Designer: Louise Turpin
Design consultant: Simon Webb

® Reader's Digest, the Pegasus logo and Reader's Digest Young Families
are registered trademarks of
The Reader's Digest Association, Inc.

We are committed both to the quality of our products
and the service we provide to our customers.
We value your comments, so please do contact us on
08705 113366 or via our website at
www.readersdigest.co.uk
If you have any comments or suggestions
about the content of our books, email us at
gbeditorial@readersdigest.co.uk

Printed in China

A Disney Enterprises/Reader's Digest Young Families Book

ISBN 978 0 276 44457 9
Book code 641-016 UP0000-1
Oracle code 504400001H.00.24